HÄGAR

the horrible

Looks ahead

ℛℛ
RAVETTE BOOKS

© 1991 King Features Syndicate, Inc.

This edition first published by Ravette Books Limited 1991

Printed and Bound
for Ravette Books Limited,
An Egmont Company,
3 Glenside Estate, Star Road, Partridge Green,
Horsham, West Sussex RH13 8RA
by Cox & Wyman Ltd, Reading

ISBN: 1 85304 340 0

HAMLET LUCKY EDDIE HÄGAR HELGA SNERT HONI

5-3

DIK BROWNE 6-3

6-8 DIK BROWNE

6-19

DIK BROWNE

DIK BROWNE 7-13

DIK BROWNE 8-8

A selection of HÄGAR books published by Ravette

POCKET BOOKS			BLACK AND WHITE LANDSCAPES	
TRIES AGAIN	£2.50		MEETS HIS MATCH	£2.50
HAS A GO	£2.50		IN A HURRY	£2.50
IN A FIX	£2.50			
ALL AT SEA	£2.50		**COLOUR LANDSCAPES**	
ON THE RAMPAGE	£2.50		TELLS IT LIKE IT IS	£2.95
GETS IT ALL	£2.50		NEVER SAY DIE	£2.95
IN A STEW	£2.50		MAKES AN ENTRANCE	£2.95
IN THE ROUGH	£2.50		WELCOME HOME	£2.95
LEADS THE WAY	£2.50			
TAKES A BREAK	£2.50		**COLOUR THEME BOOKS**	
ON HOLIDAY	£2.50		No. 1 THE GREAT GOURMET	£2.95
TAKES AIM	£2.50		No. 2 TROUBLE AND STRIFE	£2.95
MEASURE FOR MEASURE	£2.50		No. 3 TAKES A JOURNEY	£2.95
SAYS IT WITH FLOWERS	£2.50		No. 4 CHILD'S PLAY	£3.50
CHIPS AWAY	£2.50		No. 5 WHO DARES WINS	£3.50
ALBUMS			VIKING HANDBOOK	£3.95
THE HERO	£2.50			
LETS HIMSELF GO	£2.50			

All these books are available at your local bookshop or newsagent, or can be ordered direct from the publisher. Just tick the titles you require and fill in the form below. Prices and availability subject to change without notice.

Ravette Books Limited, 3 Glenside Estate, Star Road, Partridge Green, Horsham, West Sussex RH13 8RA

Please send a cheque or postal order and allow the following for postage and packing. UK: Pocket books – 45p for one book plus 20p for the second book and 15p for each additional book. Landscape series – 50p for one book plus 30p for each additional book. Other titles – 85p for one book plus 60p for each additional book.

Name ....

Address ....

....